Vulcan

VULCAN

A Picture Story by

NORMAN BATE

CHARLES SCRIBNER'S SONS New York

For Louise Deborah Hudson

Long, long ago, a steam locomotive named Vulcan pulled fast trains from city to city. His mighty drive wheels shook the rails. His whistle shrieked at the crossings. People heard him coming. They looked up and waved. "Here comes Vulcan!" they said. He roared by leaving a trail of black smoke and red hot sparks.

But now he was rusted and useless.

He stood alone and unwanted in a junkyard.

"No one wants a smoky old steam locomotive these days,"
said the junkman. "Modern trains are pulled by electric or
diesel locomotives."

"We'll have to break up old Vulcan for scrap iron," the
junkman said, "and sell him to the steel mill." Men with
torches and tools cut Vulcan into small pieces. They loaded
the pieces onto a big truck and drove to the steel mill.
No one looked at old Vulcan or waved as he passed by.

The steelmen bought the scrap iron. "Vulcan was made in
this steel mill over sixty years ago," they said. They were
sorry to see him broken up.

"Take this scrap to the open hearth furnace!" they ordered.
"We will make something new out of old Vulcan!"

Vulcan's parts were taken into the steel mill and placed in
the open hearth furnace.
The flames roared into the furnace.
Vulcan became hotter and hotter and redder and redder!
Soon he was a melting pile of scrap iron.

"Now bring new iron from the blast furnace while it's still hot!" ordered the steelmen. "We'll melt it with Vulcan's iron to make strong steel!"

Hot-metal ladles brought the new hot iron. It was quickly poured into the furnace to become part of Vulcan's molten metal.

The flames continued to roar. More iron ore was added.
For ten hours the flames burned, refining and purifying
the steel.

The metal became so white—so brilliant—that no
steelman dared look into the furnace without wearing
special glasses.

"The steel is ready!" said the steelmen. "Tap the furnace!"
The men set off an explosive charge. It blew a clay plug
out of a hole in the bottom of the furnace. Vulcan's
white hot metal poured through the hole and into a
large steel ladle.

A monstrous overhead crane picked up the ladle and
carried it to a row of molds. Each mold was filled with
molten metal from the ladle. Sparks flew in every direction.
The mill glowed red from the heat.

The ingots of hot steel were lifted from the molds and placed on a train of cars.

"Take Vulcan's metal to the soaking pits," ordered the steelmen, "and leave it there until we are ready to use it."

The soaking pits were large open top furnaces that kept the ingots at a uniform heat until they were needed.

The train was moved to the pit. One by one, the ingots
were lowered into its glowing interior.
The steelmen called their engineers and machinists and
millworkers. "We will make something special of old
Vulcan," they said. "Draw up plans and get the machinery
ready!"

When all was ready, an overhead crane carried Vulcan's ingot from the soaking pit to the mill. It was placed in front of a great machine that had huge spinning steel rollers. Vulcan was pushed toward the machine! He reached the rollers!

They gripped his edges! They spun! They squeezed!
Suddenly, Vulcan disappeared between the rollers—and
popped right out on the other side!
He was longer—and thinner—and wider than before.

Quickly, Vulcan was pushed back toward the machine.

Again, he was squeezed by the rollers!

And again, Vulcan shot right through and out the other side—much longer—and thinner—and wider!

Back and forth they pushed him. Back and forth through the mills he went. He was flattened and widened and lengthened until he became a long, wide, thin piece of plate steel.

"Now cut him up!" ordered the engineers.

Vulcan's long steel plate rested on a platform. This carried him at great speed to another machine.

Here, strong cutting wheels trimmed his edges straight and even.

He was quickly carried to a different machine. Big shears
cut him into smaller sections.

"Take Vulcan's new steel plates to the fabricating works!"
ordered the engineers. "We'll make them into something
useful!"

There were many large machines in the fabricating works.
Some were used to roll Vulcan's pieces into large cylinders
that looked like great steel drums.

Others cut and spun and shaped his pieces into curved
domes.
Still other machines punched and drilled and trimmed the
shaped pieces. Everyone was following the new plan
for Vulcan.

The engineers ordered all of the different shapes brought
to one place.
"Now we will put Vulcan together," they said.
Mechanics and fitters and welders and riveters began
their work. Piece after piece was fitted and fastened
together.

Vulcan began to take on a new shape. Bigger and bigger
he grew. At last the men were finished.

"Take Vulcan away!" ordered the engineers. "Paint him
red and black! Give him a loud whistle that can be heard
for miles! Give him a strong light to shine through the
blackest night!"

The painters came. One painted part of Vulcan black. The
other painted part of Vulcan red.

Workmen fitted a great new whistle onto his upper part.

Other workmen fastened a brilliant light high enough so that all could see it.

"We are finished," they said. "Now he is ready to be put to work!"

Vulcan was lifted by a tall crane and lowered onto a flat
car behind a powerful diesel locomotive. They traveled
across the country for many days.
When at last they stopped, another large crane lifted him
onto the deck of a great ship.

The ship sailed out to sea.

It traveled for hours and hours over rough water. When land could no longer be seen, it stopped.

"This is the place," said the captain. "This is where we drop Vulcan overboard!"

The ship's boom and winch quickly lifted Vulcan up and
dropped him over the side.

Vulcan made a tremendous splash!

Down he went—down, down under the cold water.

Suddenly, he popped back up to the surface and floated—
his black part above the water and his red part below.

A chain and anchor were attached to stop him from
drifting. The ship sailed away and left him alone to bob up
and down on the waves. Each time he went up and down
his whistle blew a mighty blast. It could be heard for miles.
At night his great light flashed through the darkness.
He was a warning buoy!

All the big ships that came in from the ocean heard
Vulcan's whistle and saw his light.
"There's old Vulcan!" the sailors would say. "We must be
nearing home!"
And most of them smiled and waved.

1687